A **Literature Kit™** F O R

Owls In The Family

● ● ● ● ● ● ● ● ● ● ● ● ● ● ● ● ●

By Farley Mowat

Written by Marie-Helen Goyetche

GRADES 3 - 4

Classroom Complete Press

P.O. Box 19729
San Diego, CA 92159
Tel: 1-800-663-3609 / Fax: 1-800-663-3608
Email: service@classroomcompletepress.com

www.classroomcompletepress.com

ISBN-13: 978-1-55319-331-9
ISBN-10: 1-55319-331-8

© 2008

Permission to Reproduce

Permission is granted to the individual teacher who purchases one copy of this book to reproduce the student activity material for use in his or her classroom only. Reproduction of these materials for colleagues, an entire school or school system, or for commercial sale is <u>strictly prohibited</u>. No part of this publication may be transmitted in any form or by any means, electronic, mechanical, recording or otherwise without the prior written permission of the publisher. We acknowledge the financial support of the Government of Canada through the Book Publishing Industry Development Program (BPIDP) for our publishing activities. Printed in Canada. All rights reserved.

Critical Thinking Skills

Owls In The Family

Skills For Critical Thinking	Chapter Questions										Writing Tasks	Graphic Organizers
	1	2	3	4	5	6	7	8	9	10&11		
LEVEL 1 Knowledge												
• Identify Story Elements	✓	✓	✓	✓	✓	✓	✓	✓	✓	✓		✓
• Recall Details	✓	✓	✓	✓	✓	✓	✓	✓	✓	✓	✓	✓
• Match	✓				✓		✓					
• Sequence Events			✓			✓			✓	✓	✓	
LEVEL 2 Comprehension												
• Summarize	✓	✓	✓	✓	✓	✓	✓	✓	✓	✓	✓	✓
• State Main Idea		✓		✓			✓		✓	✓		✓
• Describe											✓	
• Classify												✓
LEVEL 3 Application												
• Plan												✓
• Infer Outcomes	✓		✓	✓	✓		✓	✓	✓	✓		
LEVEL 4 Analysis												
• Draw Conclusions	✓	✓		✓	✓	✓	✓					✓
• Identify Supporting Evidence	✓		✓		✓			✓				✓
• Infer Character Motivations		✓	✓	✓				✓	✓	✓	✓	✓
• Identify Cause and Effect										✓		✓
LEVEL 5 Synthesis												
• Predict	✓	✓	✓	✓	✓	✓	✓	✓	✓	✓		
• Design											✓	
• Create						✓					✓	
• Write An Alternative Ending To		✓					✓		✓	✓	✓	
LEVEL 6 Evaluation												
• State & Defend An Opinion					✓			✓	✓	✓	✓	
• Make Judgements	✓		✓	✓		✓			✓	✓		✓

Based on Bloom's Taxonomy

© CLASSROOM COMPLETE PRESS

Contents

FREE!

✔ **6 BONUS Activity Pages!** Additional worksheets for your students
✔ **3 BONUS Overhead Transparencies!** For use with your projection system

- Go to our website: **www.classroomcompletepress.com/bonus**
- Enter item CC2307 – Owls In The Family
- Enter pass code CC2307D for Activity Pages. CC2307A for Overheads.

Assessment Rubric

Owls In The Family

Student's Name: _____ Assignment: _____ Level: _____

Criteria	Level 1	Level 2	Level 3	Level 4
Comprehension of Novel	Demonstrates a limited understanding of the novel	Demonstrates a basic understanding of the novel	Demonstrates a good understanding of the novel	Demonstrates a thorough understanding of the novel
Content • Information and details relevant to focus	Elements incomplete; key details missing	Some elements complete; details missing	All required elements completed; key details contain some description	All required elements completed; enough description for clarity
Style • Effective word choice and originality • Precise language	Little variety in word choice. Language vague and imprecise	Some variety in word choice. Language somewhat vague and imprecise	Good variety in word choice. Language precise and quite descriptive	Writer's voice is apparent throughout. Excellent choice of words. Precise language.
Conventions • Spelling, language, capitalization, punctuation	Errors seriously interfere with the writer's purpose	Repeated errors in mechanics and usage	Some errors in convention	Few errors in convention

STRENGTHS:

WEAKNESSES:

NEXT STEPS:

Teacher Guide

Our resource has been created for ease of use by both **TEACHERS** *and* **STUDENTS** *alike.*

Introduction

Owls in the Family is a heart felt story about a young boy named Billy, his two pet owls Weeps and Wol and a dog called Mutt. Read this adventurous story about how animals and humans communicate, develop and establish relationships. It is funny and witty. This story also blends in well with animals and weather as cross curricular theme in both science and math as well as in language arts. This story is rich in details and gives the reader some insight on the simple life in rural Saskatchewan, Canada. Award winning Farley Mowat continues the tradition in another exciting novel for animal lovers.

How Is Our Literature Kit™ Organized?

STUDENT HANDOUTS

Chapter Activities *(in the form of reproducible worksheets)* make up the majority of this resource. For each chapter or group of chapters there are BEFORE YOU READ activities and AFTER YOU READ activities.

- The BEFORE YOU READ activities prepare students for reading by setting a purpose for reading. They stimulate background knowledge and experience, and guide students to make connections between what they know and what they will learn. Important concepts and vocabulary from the chapter(s) are also presented.

- The AFTER YOU READ activities check students' comprehension and extend their learning. Students are asked to give thoughtful consideration of the text through creative and evaluative short-answer questions and journal prompts.

Six **Writing Tasks** and three **Graphic Organizers** are included to further develop students' critical thinking and writing skills, and analysis of the text. (*See page 6 for suggestions on using the Graphic Organizers.*) The **Assessment Rubric** (*page 4*) is a useful tool for evaluating students' responses to the Writing Tasks and Graphic Organizers.

PICTURE CUES

This resource contains three main types of pages, each with a different purpose and use. A **Picture Cue** at the top of each page shows, at a glance, what the page is for.

Teacher Guide
- Information and tools for the teacher

Student Handout
- Reproducible worksheets and activities

Easy Marking™ Answer Key
- Answers for student activities

EASY MARKING™ ANSWER KEY

Marking students' worksheets is fast and easy with this **Answer Key**. Answers are listed in columns – just lineup the column with its corresponding worksheet, as shown, and see how every question matches up with its answer!

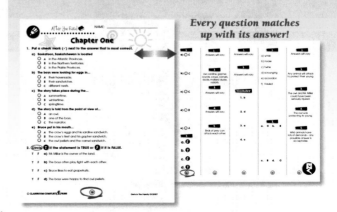

Every question matches up with its answer!

Before You Teach

1,2,3
Graphic Organizer Transparencies

The three **Graphic Organizer Transparencies** included in this Literature Kit™ are especially suited to a study of *Owl in the Family*. Below are suggestions for using each organizer in your classroom, or they may be adapted to suit the individual needs of your students. The transparencies can be used on an overhead projector in teacher-led activities, and/or photocopied for use as student worksheets. To evaluate students' responses to any of the organizers, you may wish to use the **Assessment Rubric** (*on page 4*).

The 5 W's

This graphic organizer is an excellent tool to have students go back and analyse the story. Have students fill out the information based on the questions provided on the lefthand column. Children who are exposed to different components of a story such as in the 5W's are more likely to reproduce the same pattern when writing their own stories.

Found on Page 53.

*K*W*L*

In the book *Owls in the Family*, a lot of information is available on owls. In this graphic organizer, the students will be able to collect the information they have read during the book and write it in Part I in the KNOW column. In Part II – The students are ask to list all the unanswered questions they have pertaining to owls. The students are allowed to do a basic research either in books or on the Internet. They are asked to record what they have discovered or learned in Part III Learning column.
Found on Page 54.

WOL AND HIS TRICKS

Wol had quite a few encounters. The students are asked to identify with whom the encounter is with, and what does the student retain about this encounter. Students should be able to realize that, for example, Wol amuses himself by teasing the other animals and people.

Found on Page 55.

Bloom's Taxonomy* for Reading Comprehension

The activities in this resource engage and build the full range of thinking skills that are essential for students' reading comprehension. Based on the six levels of thinking in Bloom's Taxonomy, questions are given that challenge students to not only recall what they have read, but move beyond this to understand the text through higher-order thinking. By using higher-order skills of application, analysis, synthesis and evaluation, students become active readers, drawing more meaning from the text, and applying and extending their learning in more sophisticated ways.

This **Literature Kit**™, therefore, is an effective tool for any Language Arts program. Whether it is used in whole or in part, or adapted to meet individual student needs, this resource provides teachers with the important questions to ask, inspiring students' interest, creativity, and promoting meaningful learning.

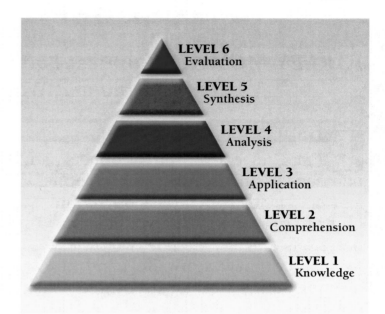

BLOOM'S TAXONOMY:
6 LEVELS OF THINKING

Bloom's Taxonomy is a widely used tool by educators for classifying learning objectives, and is based on the work of Benjamin Bloom.

Teaching Strategies   INDEPENDENT, SMALL GROUP OR WHOLE CLASS STUDY

This study guide contains the following activities:

Before Reading Activities: themes are introduced and thought-provoking questions put forward for the students to consider.

Vocabulary Activities: new and unfamiliar words are introduced and reviewed.

After Reading Questions: the first part of this section includes short answer questions dealing with the content of the play. The second part features questions that are more open-ended and feature concepts from the higher order of Bloom's Taxonomy.

Writing Tasks: creative writing assignments based on Bloom's Taxonomy that relate to the plot of the particular scenes

Graphic Organizers/Overheads: three full-page reproducible sheets. One has been designed as an

alternative to the traditional book report.

Bonus Sheets are also available online.

A **comprehension quiz** is also included comprised of short-answer questions.

The study guide can be used in a variety of ways in the classroom depending on the needs of the students and teacher. The teacher may choose to use an independent reading approach with students capable of working independently. It also works well with small groups, with most of the lessons being quite easy to follow, and finally in other situations, teachers will choose to use it with their entire class.

Teachers may wish to have their students keep a daily reading log so that they might record their daily progress and reflections.

Summary of the Story ⭐

FARLEY MOWAT's funniest book about a boy and two rescued owls named Wol and Weeps.

Billy loves all animals and he has rats, mice, over thirty gophers and two dogs. It only seems natural that he and his friends search the sloughs and bluffs to find owlets. In two different occasions, the boys rescue two owlets from an untimely death. Billy ends up keeping both owlets for over three years.

The adventures the boys and the owls have together are not the typical boy/dog story. Participating in the local Pet Parade, having his owls following him to school and having an owl arrive for dinner with a skunk are only a few funny incidents in Owls in the Family. The story is a hoot!

Suggestions for Further Reading

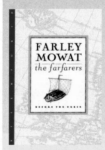

WRITINGS BY FARLEY MOWAT
People of the Deer (1952; revised 1975)
The Regiment (1955)
Lost in the Barrens (1956)
The Dog Who Wouldn't Be (1957)
Coppermine Journey: An Account of a Great Adventure (1958)
Grey Seas Under: The Perilous Rescue Missions of a North Atlantic Salvage Tug (1959)
The Desperate People (1959; revised 1999)
Ordeal by Ice (1960)

OWLS IN THE FAMILY (1961)
The Serpent's Coil: (1961); The Black Joke (1962); Never Cry Wolf (1963; West Viking (1965); The Curse of the Viking Grave (1966); Canada North (1967); The Polar Passion (1967); This Rock Within the Sea (1968); The Boat Who Wouldn't Float (1969); The Siberians (1970); Sibir: My Discovery of Siberia (1970); World of Farley Mowat (1970); A Whale for the Killing (1972); Tundra (1973); Wake of the Great Sealers (1973); The Snow Walker (1975); Canada North Now (1976); And No Birds Sang (1979); Sea of Slaughter (1984); My Discovery of America (1985); Virunga: The Passion of Dian Fossey (1987); Woman in the Mists (1987); The New Founde Land (1989); My Father's Son (1993); Born Naked (1994); Aftermath: Travels in a Post-War World (1995); Rescue the Earth! (1998); The Farfarers: Before the Norse (1998); The Alban Quest (1999); Walking on the Land (2000); High Latitudes: An Arctic Journey (2002); No Man's River (2004); Bay of Spirits: A Love Story (2006)

List of Vocabulary

CHAPTER 1

bluffs, cawing, dot, haversack, outskirts, pellets, scuttled, sloughs

CHAPTER 2

accordion, blind, hauled, noose, scrounging, snarl, twine, whisk

CHAPTER 3

chinook, funeral, hissed, miserable, nesting, owlet, pelting, skyrockets

CHAPTER 4

coward, fascinated, latch, persuaded, porridge, staggered

CHAPTER 5

cocked, educate, mauling, mottled, penned, ruckus, skidded, stalled, waddling

CHAPTER 6

bur, britches, bucking, bronco, convincing, hitch, sponsor

CHAPTER 7

absent-minded, amble, ornery, pestered, scoot, strutting, tolerate

CHAPTER 8

headquarters, hobos, plastered, shucked, steep, torment

CHAPTER 9

airborne, expedition, mannered, occasion, peered, ructions, yelp

CHAPTER 10

ammunition, caravan, deck, expanse, galley, mast, reed, rumble seats, schooner

CHAPTER 11

cayuse, mincing, moving, suspicious

Farley Mowat

Farley Mowat... is an author you are likely to hear and read a lot about. He was born on May 12, 1921 in Belleville, Ontario.

His family moved to Saskatoon Saskatchewan, where he learned a lot about nature and animals. During his teenage years, he wrote a column about birds for a local newspaper. His family moved back to Ontario. He served for the Canadian Army during World War II.

Upon his return from the war, he entered the University of Toronto to study biology. He graduated in 1949.

In 1952, his book *People of the Deer* was published and his writing career blossomed.

Farley has written over 40 books, now published in over 52 different languages. Although he writes most of his books for adults, he has written several award winning children's books.

If you enjoyed *Owls in the Family*, other stories such as *The Dog Who Wouldn't Be* (1957) and *Lost in the Barrens* (1956) are sure to interest you as well.

Did You Know..?

- In 1981, he was made an Officer of the Order of Canada.
- Lost in *the Barrens* (1956) won the GOVERNOR GENERAL'S AWARD
- Many works are autobiographical: *The Dog Who Wouldn't Be* (1957) and *Owls in the Family* (1961).

Chapter One

1. By looking at the book, we know Farley Mowat is the author, the title is Owls in the Family and there's an owl sitting on a boy's head. What do you think this book is about? Where do you think the story takes place? What genre of book will this book be; mystery, adventure, etc?

_____

_____

_____

2. How do you feel about owls? What is the closest you have been to an owl? What information do you know about owls? What would you like to discover?

_____

_____

_____

Vocabulary

Connect each vocabulary word to its definition.

1	**haversack**	the outside of town	A
2	**pellets**	lakes and ponds	B
3	**outskirts**	to mark remote scattered spots	C
4	**dot**	a one-shoulder knapsack	D
5	**bluffs**	birds of prey regurgitate body parts that can't be digested	E
6	**sloughs**	a high steep bank/cliff	F

Chapter One

1. Put a check mark (✓) next to the answer that is most correct.

a) Saskatoon, Saskatchewan is located

○ **A**   in the Atlantic Provinces.

○ **B**   in the Northern Territories.

○ **C**   in the Prairie Provinces.

b) The boys were looking for eggs in...

○ **A**   their haversacks.

○ **B**   their sandwiches.

○ **C**   different nests.

c) The story takes place during the...

○ **A**   summertime.

○ **B**   wintertime.

○ **C**   springtime.

d) The story is told from the point of view of...

○ **A**   an owl.

○ **B**   one of the boys.

○ **C**   the narrator.

e) Bruce put in his mouth...

○ **A**   the crow's eggs and his sardine sandwich.

○ **B**   the crow's feet and his gopher sandwich.

○ **C**   the owl pellets and the camel sandwich.

2. Circle T if the statement is TRUE or F if it is FALSE.

T   F   **a)** Mr. Millar is the owner of the land.

T   F   **b)** The boys often play fight with each other.

T   F   **c)** Bruce likes to eat grapefruits.

T   F   **d)** The boys were happy to find owl pellets.

Chapter One

Answer each question with a complete sentence.

1. How else could Bruce have taken the eggs down from the nest?

_____

_____

2. The boys mention eight animals in Chapter One, can you list them?

_____

_____

3. Why do you think the boys wanted owls for pets? Is that a good idea or not? Why?

_____

_____

4. Have you ever seen an owl pellet? How could you get some owl pellets?

_____

_____

5. Why would the crows attack the owl?

_____

_____

Journaling Prompt

The boys are planning to have an owl as a pet. Read information about owls. Write up a list to convince your parents that having an owl for a pet is a good idea. Write a second list stating why it is not a good idea to have an owl as a pet. Would it be easy or not to convince your parents to allow you to have an owl in the house? Explain your answer.

Chapter Two

1. Why do you think the father answered "Oh NO! Not owls too."?

_____

_____

2. What do you think the boys would have done with the eggs if they were still intact? Is taking eggs from a bird's nest dangerous? Explain.

_____

_____

Vocabulary

Circle the word that best matches the meaning of the underlined word in each of the following sentences.

1. Billy's dad was a little **peeved** to have so many pets in the garage.

    a) happy   **b)** angry   **c)** worried   **d)** afraid

2. Mr. Miller and the boys built a **hiding tent** in a platform placed in another tree.

    a) noose   **b)** twine   **c)** bluff   **d)** blind

3. Someone who didn't **tell them the truth** about owls knowing how to count.

    a) liar   **b)** robber   **c)** veterinarian   **d)** reposed

4. Mr. Miller tried to **adjust the lens** of the camera while hiding in the tent.

    a) climb   **b)** fall   **c)** focus   **d)** shoot

Chapter Two

1. Use the words in the box to answer each question.

scrounging	hauled	whisk	twine	accordion	noose

a) How did the gophers get back into their holes?

b) What type of knot did the boys make to help them catch gophers?

c) What type of string did the boys use?

d) How did the boys get the wood?

e) What instrument did Billy see when Mr. Miller was drinking?

f) How did the boys and Mr. Miller bring up the tent in the tree?

2. Which answer best describes...

a) How Billy felt about Mutt?

_____ A   Mutt was upset.

_____ B   Mutt was like a friend.

_____ C   Mutt was part of the family.

b) How Mr. Miller explained his encounter with the owl?

_____ A   laughing

_____ B   snarling

_____ C   choking

c) How Mr. Miller felt when the owl left with his hat?

_____ A   hungry

_____ B   thirsty

_____ C   sleepy

d) How the owl felt when she saw a man climbing up her tree?

_____ A   didn't bother her

_____ B   she attacked once

_____ C   she attacked twice

Chapter Two

Answer each question with a complete sentence.

1. How would you have dealt with the angry owl?

_____

_____

2. What other types of animals also attack to protect their young?

_____

_____

3. What would have happened if the owl crashed into Mr. Miller?

_____

_____

4. Why did the owl attack if Mr. Miller only wanted to take pictures?

_____

_____

5. What type of pet does a baby owl make? What kind of needs would an owl have?

_____

_____

Journaling Prompt

After the experience of seeing the owl attack twice, Mr. Miller told the boys there were three half-grown owls in the nest. Continue the story. Will the boys and Mr. Miller go back and get the owls? How will they do this? Will anyone get hurt? What mishaps can happen? Make your story dramatic and add lots of adventure words.

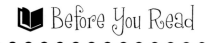

Chapter Three

1. How do you think Bruce, Billy and Mr. Miller will capture the three half-grown owls? What do you predict the mother will do?

_____

_____

2. How do you feel about the fact that the boys and Mr. Miller are trying to capture the birds? Explain your answer.

_____

_____

Vocabulary

Read each sentence below. Replace the word in brackets with a word from the list.

funeral	owlet	pelting	skyrockers	chinook

1. (Storms) _____ come down out of the Rocky Mountains in Alberta and blow right across Saskatchewan.

2. Only one (young owl) _____ survived the terrible tragedy.

3. Billy thought he could use (firecrackers) _____ to scare the old owl away from the nest.

4. The (ceremony) _____ is held to honor the dead person before the burial.

5. The (removing) _____ of an animal's pelt is done to keep the fur.

Chapter Three

1. **Put a check mark (✓) next to the answer that is most correct.**

a) **What did the boys feed the owl?**

- ○ **A** meat, bread and dead fish.
- ○ **B** meat, fish and eggs.
- ○ **C** meat, bread, dead mice.

b) **The last young owl found was alive. He most probably...**

- ○ **A** was the first egg laid and hatched.
- ○ **B** was the middle egg to be laid and hatched.
- ○ **C** was the last egg laid and hatched.

c) **What did Billy name the young owl?**

- ○ **A** Winnie
- ○ **B** Wol
- ○ **C** Christopher

2. **Number the events from ① to ⑤ in the order they occurred.**

☐ **a)** While the owl was watching the gophers, Billy thought up what name to give the owl.

☐ **b)** The third young owl was bigger than the others and he was still alive.

☐ **c)** The chinook took Mr. Miller's blind and brought the owl's nest down to the ground.

☐ **d)** The boys found two dead, wet and cold half-grown owls.

☐ **e)** Billy suggested he bring the owl home but the owl would belong to all three boys.

Chapter Three

Answer each question with a complete sentence.

1. What would you have done if you had found dead owls?

_____

_____

2. What do you think happened to the mother owl? Will she return?

_____

_____

3. Why do you think Billy mentioned that the owl belonged to all three boys?

_____

_____

4. Can you imagine how the owl felt?

_____

_____

5. Why did the owl swallow the dead mice whole in one piece?

_____

_____

Journaling Prompt

Billy sensed that Bruce was a little jealous about the owl staying close to him. Jealousy is feeling upset at someone for having something that you would also like. Sometimes these feelings are just in passing, other times, some people get really upset and angry. Some even stop speaking because of jealous feelings. When was the last time you felt jealous? What happened? How was the situation resolved? How do you control your jealousy now?

📖 Before You Read
••••••••••••••••••••

Chapter Four

1. Do you think the owl will eat the gophers? Explain your answer.

_____

_____

_____

2. How well do you think the owl will live inside an enclosed area?

_____

_____

_____

Vocabulary

Complete each sentence with a word from the list.

coward	latch	porridge	staggered	persuaded	fascinated

1. Wol was _____ by the thirty gophers in the summerhouse.

2. After she served Billy's _____, Offy was in for a big surprise.

3. The tiny owl finally _____ to his feet.

4. Billy tightly closed his bedroom door but the _____ must have slipped.

5. The little gopher wasn't going to die a _____; he turned and bit Wol.

6. Nothing could have _____ Wol to go back down to where the gophers were.

Chapter Four

1. Use the words in the box to answer each question.

Georgie Barnes	Ophelia	Wol	Weeps	the gopher

a) Who bit Wol?

b) What did Billy call his new owl?

c) What is the maid's name?

d) Who is the boy that was throwing stones at the owl?

e) Who was lonely without Billy, Bruce and Murray?

2. Circle T if the statement is TRUE or F if it is FALSE.

T   F   **a)** Bruce and Murray found another owl.

T   F   **b)** Offy is Billy's mom.

T   F   **c)** Billy found an owl that was being mistreated.

T   F   **d)** Billy fed the owl some porridge.

T   F   **e)** Wol and Weeps loved to eat all the gophers they could get.

T   F   **f)** Billy's dad warned Billy not to get any more owls.

T   F   **g)** Billy only wanted two owls.

NAME: _____

Chapter Four

Answer each question with a complete sentence.

1. What other way could Billy have approached Georgie Barns?

_____

_____

2. Do you think it was smart for the boys to mistreat the owl?

_____

_____

3. If you were Georgie Barnes, what would you have done?

_____

_____

4. Do you believe Billy's father was fair with Billy because of Offy leaving? What do you think his mother would have said?

_____

_____

5. If you were the parents, what would you have done?

_____

_____

Journaling Prompt

Billy's father threatened Billy that if the owl were to return inside the house, the owl would be going into the roasting pan. Have you ever heard of anyone eating owl?

Have you ever had a meal where your parents, (or other family member) have told you the meal was one thing but it really turned out to be something else? How did you react? Was the meal good? If this situation never happened to you, how do you predict you would react if someone tried it on you?

Before You Read

Chapter Five

1. Do you think that Billy was honest when he said he only wanted two owls? Explain your answer.

_____

_____

_____

2. How would you react with 2 owls for pets? Would you have known what to do with the sick owl?

_____

_____

_____

Vocabulary

Connect each vocabulary word to its definition.

1	mauling		to move clumsily	A
2	penned		to teach how	B
3	educate		to haul by dragging	C
4	ruckus		to shut in/enclose	D
5	skidded		colored spots or blotches	E
6	waddling		to keep an ear out/tilted	F
7	mottled		to handle roughly	G
8	cocked		disturbance – lots of noise	H

NAME: _____ _____

Chapter Five

1. Put a check mark (✓) next to the answer that is most correct.

a) With what did Wol have a scuffle?

○ **A** a gopher

○ **B** a cat

○ **C** two boys

b) What vegetable does Wol hate?

○ **A** figs

○ **B** potatoes

○ **C** parsnips

c) Which owl doesn't know how to fly?

○ **A** Wol

○ **B** Weeps

○ **C** both Wol and Weeps

2. Which word best describes the character(s) when.

a) When Wol was stuck at the top of the tree?

_____ A excited

_____ B unhappy

_____ C tired and cranky

b) What the man thought of the owl that couldn't fly?

_____ A crazy

_____ B upset

_____ C nauseous

c) Billy, when Wol actually flew

_____ A laughing

_____ B ashamed

_____ C guilty

d) Weeps, about flying

_____ A he can't

_____ B he can

_____ C he never stops

Chapter Five

Answer each question with a complete sentence.

1. How come the owls didn't know how to fly? Why didn't Billy show them?

_____

_____

2. Why do you think Weeps believed that he couldn't do anything by himself?

_____

_____

3. What's the closest you've been to owl?

_____

_____

4. What do you think we can learn from Wol's behavior?

_____

_____

5. What important points do you recall from the owls and their size?

_____

_____

Journaling Prompt

By mid June, Wol was a little taller than Weeps and stood about two feet high; but his wingspread was nearly five feet across. There are 12 inches in each foot. Each inch equals 2.54 centimeters. How tall is Wol in centimeters? How wide is his wingspread in centimeters.

Chapter Six

1. How long do you think the owls will stay with Billy and his family?

_____

_____

_____

2. How would you react if your friend went about town with an owl hanging on their bike?

_____

_____

_____

Vocabulary

Circle the word that best matches the meaning of the underlined word in each of the following sentences.

1. T. Eaton Department Store **sponsored** the pet parade.

   a) supported   **b)** paid and organized   **c)** encouraged

2. The boys didn't need **convincing** to participate in the parade.

   a) persuade   **b)** talk out of   **c)** arguing

3. Bruce would have gotten his **britches** tanned if he had lost the snake.

   a) gloves, hand   **b)** hair, head   **c)** trousers, pants

4. Bruce grabbed the shoebox and stuck to it like a **bur**.

   a) something that sticks **b)** something hot   **c)** something loose

Chapter Six

1. Use the words in the box to answer each question.

| Rattlesnake | a Clydesdale horse | Wol and Weeps | Rex | Mutt |

a) Who did Murray try to paint stripes on?

b) Who was going to wear the doll clothes?

c) Who was lucky to have a real harness?

d) Who wore the blanket with *Baby* written on it?

e) What was in the tied-up box?

2. Number the events from ⟦1⟧ to ⟦7⟧ in the order they occurred.

a) The boys decided to build a second cage.

b) There were five judges sitting at the judges' stand.

c) T. Eaton Department Store announced their participation in the pet parade.

d) Opening the box created a huge ruckus!

e) Murray had more paint on himself than anywhere else.

f) Bruce showed up with a box written **Surprise Pet Do Not Feed.**

g) The boys spend a few days planning for everything.

Chapter Six

Answer each question with a complete sentence.

1. Do you think it was a good idea for Bruce to bring the old rattlesnake in a box? How could he have shown off the snake without causing such a ruckus?

_____

_____

2. Why do you think Murray wore more paint than Rex?

_____

_____

3. If you were judges, whom would you have given the first place prize? Justify your choice.

_____

_____

4. Can you relate to how the other reacted? What would have been your reaction?

_____

_____

5. Can you explain why the boys were disappointed for not winning first place?

_____

_____

Journaling Prompt

Create a poster to attract spectators to the T. Eaton Department Store Pet Parade. Use advertising techniques such as different fonts, pictures, drawings and words. Include important information such as the date, the time and the location.

Chapter Seven

Answer the questions in complete sentences.

1. Do you agree with Billy that they should have won first place? Explain your answer.

_____

_____

2. So far in this story, many new animals are brought home. How do you think the other animals feel about new animals coming in? How can you introduce new animals together to avoid jealousy and rivalry?

_____

_____

_____

Vocabulary

Connect each vocabulary word to its definition.

1	scoot	endure or to allow	A
2	amble	harass with petty irritations	B
3	pestered	preoccupied	C
4	tolerated	move swiftly	D
5	absentminded	having an irritable disposition	E
6	ornery	to parade showing pride	F
7	strutting	to handle roughly	G
8	fierce	to stroll	H

Chapter Seven

1. Put a check mark (✓) next to the answer that is most correct.

a) Mutt didn't get along well with Wol because...

  ○ **A** Weeps would interfere.

  ○ **B** Wol and Weeps hated dogs.

  ○ **C** Wol would play many tricks on Mutt.

b) Mutt was an old dog and he was also...

  ○ **A** a practical joker.

  ○ **B** absentminded.

  ○ **C** a skunk lover.

c) Wol would often...

  ○ **A** sneak up on Mutt while Mutt was sleeping.

  ○ **B** sleep while Mutt would sleep.

  ○ **C** run after skunks while Mutt did the same thing.

d) The only animal Wol would viciously attack was...

  ○ **A** dogs.

  ○ **B** skunks.

  ○ **C** gophers and rats.

2. Circle T if the statement is TRUE or F if it is FALSE.

T F **a)** Billy had many brothers and sisters.

T F **b)** Mutt protected Weeps from other dogs.

T F **c)** Weeps played tricks on Mutt all the time.

T F **d)** Wol loved to eat skunk.

T F **e)** Billy would feed skunk to Wol and Weeps every week.

Answer each question with a complete sentence.

1. Have you ever had an encounter with a skunk? What happened?

_____

_____

2. What arrangements could Billy have made to stop Wol from playing jokes on Mutt? Why do you think Wol played these jokes on Mutt?

_____

_____

3. Why do you think Mutt was so good to Weeps? What connections do you make when you hear about Mutt protecting Weeps?

_____

_____

4. What can you do to prevent skunks from spraying their lovely perfume?

_____

_____

5. What suggestions can you suggest to anyone who has been sprayed by a skunk?

_____

_____

Journaling Prompt

Rewrite the dining room scene where Wol brings a dead skunk for supper. Change the situation where maybe the new setting is in a restaurant, during a wedding or an outdoor birthday party. Add more people, more turmoil and more chaos. What new mishaps happen in your dining room scene?

NAME: _____

Chapter Eight

1. Have you ever had a treehouse or an enclosed area that was your own secret hiding place? Where is it? Is it a safe place?

_____

_____

2. What other adventures do you predict will happen with Wol and Weeps?

_____

_____

Vocabulary

Complete each sentence with a word from the list.

plastered	steep	tormented	hobos	shucked

1. The crows caused a lot of persistent distress and _____ Wol.

2. The banks of the river were high and very _____.

3. When Wol went into the water, his feathers were wet, shinny and stuck to his body as if they had been _____ there.

4. A homeless and penniless vagabond is also known as a _____.

5. The boys were in a hurry to take off their clothes so they could go swimming, they _____ off their clothes.

Chapter Eight

1. **Use the words in the box to answer each question.**

| coyotes | buffaloes | Mounties |
| headquarters | two boys | prairie chickens |

☐	**a)**	What did the boys call their digging caves?
☐	**b)**	What was on the other side of the river banks?
☐	**c)**	Who came after Bruce and Billy?
☐	**d)**	What animals were on that land in the olden times?
☐	**e)**	Who chased the Native?
☐	**f)**	What was hiding underneath Wol and thought he was their mother?

2. **Which word best describes the action...**

a) How did Bruce feel when Wol let out a scream?

_____ **A** it scared him

_____ **B** it made him laugh

_____ **C** it made him cry

b) What the boy did to Billy?

_____ **A** pinched him

_____ **B** hit him

_____ **C** tripped and sat on him

c) What action did the boy do to Bruce?

_____ **A** twisted his leg

_____ **B** twisted his arm

_____ **C** twisted his knee

d) How did Wol feel with the chickens at his feet?

_____ **A** tired

_____ **B** silly

_____ **C** inspired

NAME: _____ _____

Chapter Eight

Answer each question with a complete sentence.

1. How would you have gotten out of the situation with the two boys?

_____

_____

2. Can you recall how Wol felt having the prairie chickens at his feet? Why did they do this?

_____

_____

3. What could have happened if the boys had not been afraid of the owl's screech?

_____

_____

4. Where do you think Weeps was during all this time? What do you think his reaction would have been?

_____

_____

Journaling Prompt

At the end of Chapter Eight, two boys had been trying to bully Billy and Bruce into telling them where their cave was. Luckily for Bruce and Billy, Wol came to their rescue.

Have you ever been in a similar situation? How did the situation end? Did you discuss the situation? Recount your experience. Write about the ways someone can go about defending themselves against bullies. Develop a slogan, poster, banner.

Chapter Nine

1. Have you ever been to Saskatoon, Saskatchewan? How different do you think this city differs from yours? How do you think it is similar?

_____

_____

2. How long do you predict the owls will stay at Billy's? Do you think they will leave and go back and live their lives in nature? Why or why not?

_____

_____

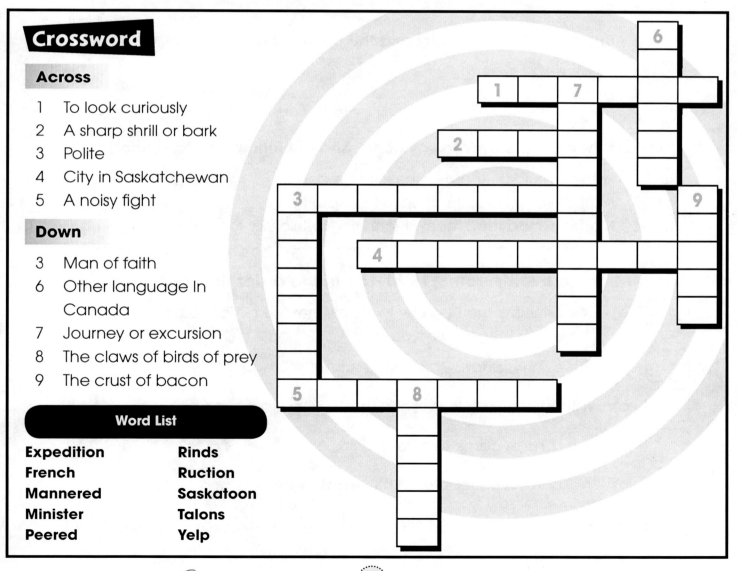

Crossword

Across

1 To look curiously
2 A sharp shrill or bark
3 Polite
4 City in Saskatchewan
5 A noisy fight

Down

3 Man of faith
6 Other language In Canada
7 Journey or excursion
8 The claws of birds of prey
9 The crust of bacon

Word List

Expedition	**Rinds**
French	**Ruction**
Mannered	**Saskatoon**
Minister	**Talons**
Peered	**Yelp**

Chapter Nine

1. Put a check mark (✓) next to the answer that is most correct.

a) Wol never realized that he was an owl, he acted more like...

○ **A** people
○ **B** dogs
○ **C** gophers

b) Who was talking to mom about Billy?

○ **A** the Minister
○ **B** The Principal
○ **C** Fifi

c) What subject did Fifi teach Billy and the other kids?

○ **A** Fractions
○ **B** French
○ **C** Fitness

d) How did they get the owls to say home and not follow Billy to school?

○ **A** Father would tie them to the kitchen door.
○ **B** Mother would lock them up in the closet.
○ **C** Mother would feed them bacon rinds while Billy took off.

2. Number the events from ① to ⑥ in the order they occurred.

[ ] **a)** The principal warned Billy that he'd get the police to take care of the owls if they showed up again at school.

[ ] **b)** The owls kept following Billy to school.

[ ] **c)** Without wanting to Wol hurt the Minister a few times.

[ ] **d)** The Minister came over for a visit.

[ ] **e)** Wol had an encounter with the postman.

[ ] **f)** Wol had an encounter with Fifi.

Chapter Nine

Answer each question with a complete sentence.

1. Why do you think the owls kept getting into trouble?

_____

_____

_____

2. How do you think Billy felt about the owls getting into trouble? Why didn't he just get rid of them?

_____

_____

_____

3. If you were Billy's parents, what would you have done? Would you accept all this from Billy, the kids and the owls? How would you feel about all of this?

_____

_____

_____

4. How do you think Wol felt after the incidents? Do you think animals can feel *remorse*?

_____

_____

_____

Journaling Prompt

Wol and Weeps had encounters with the Minister, the postman, Fifi the teacher and the principal. Choose one of these characters and write their version of the situation. How did they feel? What did they hear? What did they smell? Make the situation funnier or more dramatic than the version in the book.

 Before You Read

Chapters Ten and Eleven

NAME: _____

1. Have you ever experienced moving to a different city, town, district or country? How, when and where did you relocate to?

_____

_____

2. How do you think changing houses, schools and friends would go over with you and your family?

_____

_____

Vocabulary

Connect each vocabulary word to its definition.

1	**galley**		the roof	A
2	**deck**		the kitchen	B
3	**ammunition**		a flag pole	C
4	**mast**		a traveling living quarters	D
5	**caravan**		primers fired from guns	E
6	**expanse**		a vessel	F
7	**schooner**		spread out in the open	G

After You Read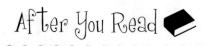

Chapters Ten and Eleven

1. Put a check mark (✓) next to the answer that is most correct.

a) What type of food did Weeps enjoy at Bruce's farm?

○ **A** minced meat for Shepard's pie.

○ **B** fox meat.

○ **C** scraps of meat that was food for the foxes.

b) How did Billy reassure Wol?

○ **A** he tickled him behind his horns

○ **B** he tickled his claws

○ **C** he tickled underneath his wings

c) Bruce's family moved two hundred miles to the northwest, why?

○ **A** to live on a geese farm

○ **B** to live on a muskrat farm.

○ **C** to live on a fox farm.

2. Which word best describes the situation.

a) How Billy, Bruce and dad felt about the crows?

○ **A** happy

○ **B** angry

○ **C** indifferent

b) What Billy's dad decided to do with the crows?

○ **A** eat them

○ **B** tickle them

○ **C** shoot them

c) The owls, at Bruce's farm

○ **A** they were in good hands

○ **B** they were in bad hands

○ **C** they were in the wild

d) Billy, how he felt about leaving his owls

○ **A** sad

○ **B** mad

○ **C** jealous

Chapters Ten and Eleven

Answer each question with a complete sentence.

1. If you were in Billy's shoes, what other alternatives could you have to find a new and good home for the owls?

   _____

   _____

2. What are other ways they could have used to distract the owls?

   _____

   _____

3. Have you ever lost a pet? What did you do? How did you deal with it?

   _____

   _____

4. What do you think Billy learned from this owl experience?

   _____

   _____

5. What important points do you retain about dealing with wild animals?

   _____

   _____

Journaling Prompt

Place yourself in Bruce's shoes. You are now Wol's and Weeps' caregiver. You got them when Billy moved to Toronto when the owls were three but now the owls are much older. Write a letter to Billy giving him news about the owls. How are the owls? Write something funny or sad about the owls.

Chapter 1

For this writing task you will need a camera, film and an animal.

Take your camera and take pictures. Get pictures of your animal sleeping, eating, playing and doing other special things that your animal does (10–12 pictures).

Create a scrapbook about your animal. Along with your pictures, add information as to how long your animal should live, what it should eat, any special care it needs. In your scrapbook, include a feeding schedule, a vet appointment checklist and other important information relating to your animal.

If you don't have a pet, be creative and adopt a snail, a fly, a spider, an ant or any other living creature.

Chapter 5

Take the position of Wol the owl or Weeps the owl. Take a passage from the book and rewrite it in the owl's point-of-view. Describe the misunderstandings, the torments, the wants, the needs and desires coming from one of the owls. If you choose a funny passage, did the owl think it was funny?

Take some wrapping or kraft paper, fold in half and draw a life size owl. Cut out both sides and staple along the edge. Leave some room on the side and stuff the owl with rolled up newspaper balls, once stuffed, staple shut. Decorate the owl using markers. Glue sunflowers seeds or feather on the owl's belly.

Now you have a written passage and the mascot to go along with your passage.

Chapter 6

Reread the passage in Chapter 6, where the Mounties, the people, the many different kinds of animals get together for the parade. The lid on the box is removed and a calm parade turns into chaos and a stampede with everyone running all over the place.

Rewrite the passage by adding more dialog and turn your passage into a Reader's Theater.

How did people react? How did people feel? Were they all scared?

Present your Reader's Theater to younger students and let them enjoy.

📝 Writing Task # 4

Chapter 7

Wol's favorite treat was skunk. He was kind enough to bring a skunk home on two occasions. Write a promotional campaign for the new line of skunk perfume with Wol as the spokes person.

Create a poster advertising the new perfume, along with a slogan and catchy lines.

Once you have presented your campaign to your fellow classmates. Create a graph on how many kids would be tempted, based on your campaign to buy this new perfume (you have to be convincing) to try and maybe buy the new perfume. What percent of kids would like to buy it? What percentage of kids wouldn't buy it?

Chapter 9

Many people have been heard saying that owls are lucky animals. Write a legend, fable or a fairy tale about Wol the Great Owl.

Write about how this animal can make others happy and lucky.

Don't forget to write a short chant, sung by the owl when activating the luck.

Chapter 11

Choose your favorite scene from Owls in the Family. Is it the stampede scene, the camping trip scene, the skunk scene, the classroom scene or maybe it's the scene with the Minister?

Using a shoebox as your stage, recreate the scene. Use tempera paints, scraps of paper, miniature toys and clay to decorate the inside of your box as closely to the scene as possible.

Write a summary of the scene on an index card and read to your audience as you display your diorama.

NAME: _____

Word Search

Find all of the words in the Word Search. Words may be horizontal, vertical or even diagonal. A few may even be backwards. Look carefully!

AIRBORNE	BLIND	BRONCO	CARAVAN	CAYUSE	CHINOOK
DECK	EDUCATE	GALLEY	HAULED	HAVERSACK	HEADQUARTERS
HOBOS	LATCH	MAST	MINCING	MISERABLE	NOOSE
ORNERY	OUTSKIRTS	OWLET	PELLETS	PERSUADED	PLASTERED
RUCKUS	SCHOONER	SLOUGHS	SPONSOR	STAGGERED	SUSPICIOUS

H	E	A	D	Q	U	A	R	T	E	R	S	L	O	U	G	H	S
A	A	S	R	T	M	N	F	S	O	V	R	M	N	V	S	U	U
V	Q	U	C	Z	R	Y	L	A	T	C	H	B	T	B	K	P	S
E	X	V	L	X	Q	V	E	M	Q	S	A	W	S	C	B	R	P
R	B	A	D	E	C	W	A	E	S	D	C	B	U	N	M	O	I
S	Q	S	R	W	D	R	S	V	B	N	E	R	T	X	I	Y	C
A	T	M	Z	U	N	M	C	Z	X	F	Q	P	L	O	S	Q	I
C	X	B	M	Z	Y	T	U	S	R	K	X	R	M	T	E	W	O
K	O	O	N	I	H	C	T	P	E	L	L	E	T	S	R	B	U
C	A	U	B	V	T	A	O	Z	N	Y	N	M	S	R	A	O	S
E	S	T	D	X	C	R	A	F	O	R	N	E	R	Y	B	L	T
D	V	S	V	O	V	A	G	N	O	W	L	E	T	E	L	S	A
U	R	K	W	P	B	V	H	V	H	Y	R	B	V	L	E	T	G
C	S	I	E	U	R	A	M	S	C	T	K	N	W	L	Z	W	G
A	T	R	Q	Z	T	N	O	O	S	E	X	Z	Q	A	C	X	E
T	R	T	A	Q	B	A	X	M	I	N	C	I	N	G	N	M	R
E	X	S	P	O	N	S	O	R	T	P	B	C	M	X	G	H	E
S	E	A	Q	N	M	Q	P	V	K	Q	M	H	Q	A	S	N	D
U	E	Q	A	I	R	B	O	R	N	E	P	O	C	N	O	R	B
Y	S	E	V	N	M	C	L	S	E	Q	V	B	N	Z	P	E	L
A	U	Z	M	V	C	B	I	Q	E	C	E	O	J	H	K	L	I
C	A	C	W	Y	U	I	O	P	Q	D	P	S	D	M	V	C	N
W	D	E	R	E	T	S	A	L	P	E	R	S	U	A	D	E	D

© CLASSROOM COMPLETE PRESS

NAME: _____

Comprehension Quiz

24

Answer each question in a complete sentence.

1. How did Billy find the first owl? How did he find the second owl?

 2

_____

_____

2. Why did Billy get to keep Wol and Weeps? What other animals did he have?

 2

_____

_____

3. What was the biggest problem with the owls? What did the owls eat?

 2

_____

_____

4. Where did Billy, Bruce and Murray show off the owls? How did they do this?

 2

_____

_____

5. What special float did they make for that special day? Who inspired them?

 2

_____

_____

6. What did Bruce bring? What happened when the lid came off the box?

 2

_____

_____

SUBTOTAL: /12

Comprehension Quiz

7. What did Wol do to the Minister? What did Wol do to the postman?

⊘ 2

_____

_____

8. What did Wol do to Fifi? What did the principal tell Billy?

⊘ 2

_____

_____

9. What was Wol's favorite pastime? What did Billy's father's friend do when he would visit?

⊘ 2

_____

_____

10. What other activities did Wol like to do? Who didn't like these activities?

⊘ 2

_____

_____

11. What did the family do in Dundurn? What happened when they were out in the canoe on the marsh?

⊘ 2

_____

_____

12. Why and where did the family move to? Who took care of the owls?

⊘ 2

_____

_____

SUBTOTAL: /12

11.

1. Answers will vary

2. Answers will vary

Vocabulary

1. D
2. E
3. A
4. C
5. B
6. F

12.

1.
a) C
b) C
c) C
d) B
e) A

2.
a. F
b. T
c. F
d. T

13.

1. Answers will vary

2. owl, sardine, gopher, coyote, crows, camels, ducks, mallard ducks, rabbits.

3. Answers will vary

4. Answers will vary

5. Birds of prey can attack each other.

14.

1. Answers will vary

2. Answers will vary

Vocabulary

1. b
2. d
3. a
4. c

15.

1.
a) whisk
b) noose
c) twine
d) scrounging
e) accordion
f) hauled

2.
a. C   b. B
c. B   d. C

16.

1. Answers will vary

2. Any animal will attack to protect their young.

3. The owl and Mr. Miller could have been seriously injured.

4. The owl was protecting its young.

5. Wild animals have lots of demands – any plausible answer is acceptable.

![EZ✔]

1. Answers will vary

2. No, hurting an animal is cruel and dangerous

3. Answers will vary

4. Answers will vary

5. Answers will vary

1.
a) the gopher
b) Weeps
c) Ophelia
d) Georgie Barnes
e) Wol

2.
a. F
b. F
c. T
d. F
e. F
f. T
g. T

---

1. Answers will vary

Answers will vary

Vocabulary

1. fascinated
2. porridge
3. staggered
4. latch
5. coward
6. persuaded

---

1. Answers will vary

2. Answers will vary

3. Not to leave anyone out.

4. Answers will vary

5. An owl has a beak, it takes and swallows. It doesn't eat and chew like us. They have no teeth.

1.
a) ○ C
b) ○ A
c) ○ B

2.
a) 3
b) 4
c) 2
d) 5
e) 1

---

1. Answers will vary

2. Answers will vary

Vocabulary

1. chinook
2. owlet
3. skyrockets
4. funeral
5. pelting

© CLASSROOM COMPLETE PRESS

23

1. Answers will vary

2. Answers will vary

Vocabulary

1. G
2. D
3. B
4. H
5. C
6. A
7. E
8. F

24

1.
a) ○ B
b) ○ C
c) ○ B

2.
a. B   b. A
c. A   d. A

25

1. Answers vary

2. Scared from his childhood and no other owl taught him what to do

3. Answers will vary

4. Answers will vary

5. Owls are huge.

26

1. Answers will vary

2. Answers will vary

Vocabulary

1. b
2. a
3. c
4. a

27

1.
a) Rex
b) Wol and Weeps
c) Mutt
d) a Clydesdale horse
e) rattlesnake

2.
a) 3
b) 7
c) 1
d) 6
e) 5
f) 2
g) 4

28

1. He could have used an aquarium or clear plastic container.

2. Not easy to paint a dog

3. Answers will vary

4. Answers will vary

5. Answers will vary

EZ✔

EZ✔

1. Answers will vary

2. Answers will vary

3. Answers will vary

4. Answers will vary

(34)

1.
a) headquarters
b) coyotes
c) two boys
d) buffaloes
e) Mounties
f) prairies chickens

2.
a. A   b. B
c. C   d. B

(33)

---

1. Answers will vary

2. Answers will vary

Vocabulary

1. tormented
2. steep
3. plastered
4. hobos
5. shucked

(32)

---

1. Answers will vary

2. Answers will vary

3. He felt his weakness

4. Stay away from them, and don't move or scare it.

5. Tomato juice or special product found at the Vet's.

(31)

1.
a) ◯ C   c) ◯ A
b) ◯ B   d) ◯ B

2.
a. F
b. T
c. F
d. T
e. F

(30)

---

1. Answers will vary

2. Answers will vary

Vocabulary

1. D
2. H
3. B
4. A
5. C
6. E
7. F
8. G

(29)

1. Answers will vary

2. Answers will vary

3. Answers will vary

4. Answers will vary

5. be kind to our animals.

40

1.
a) ⊘ C

b) ⊘ A

c) ⊘ C

2.
a) ⊘ B
b) ⊘ C

c) ⊘ A
d) ⊘ A

39

---

1. Answers will vary

2. Answers will vary

Vocabulary

1. B
2. A
3. E
4. C
5. D
6. G
7. F

38

---

1. Answers will vary

2. Answers will vary

3. Answers will vary

4. Answers will vary

37

1.
a) ⊘ A

b) ⊘ A

c) ⊘ B

d) ⊘ C

2.
a) 4
b) 3
c) 5
d) 2
e) 6
f) 1

36

---

1. Answers will vary

2. Answers will vary

Crossword

Across

1) peered
2) yelp
3) mannered
4) Saskatoon
5) ruction

Down

3) Minister
6) French
7) expedition
8) talons
9) rinds

35

EZ✓

Word Search Puzzle Answers

1. The boys found the first owl the day after a storm (chinook). The nest was on the floor along with 2 dead owlets and Wol. The boys found the second owl in a barrel, where two mean boys were throwing rocks at it.

2. Billy kept the owls because he had the space. His parents already allowed him to have 30 gophers, rats and 2 dogs.

3. The biggest problem with the owls is they followed Billy everywhere even at school. They ate meat, scraps, bacon rinds, other animals, even skunks.

4. The boys showed off the owls at the pet parade. They built cages and they dressed up the animals.

5. They made two circus like cages. The Bailey Brothers Circus inspired them.

6. Bruce brought a tightly closed box with a rattlesnake inside. The parade ended in chaos and a stampede by the crowd when they realized there was a rattlesnake in the box

7. The Minister scared Wol while Wol was on his shoulder. To keep his balance, he dug his talons into the Minister. The postman walked into Wol and kicked him, Wol spread his wings and clomped the postman on the shins.

8. Wol entered Fifi's classroom by the window and when he landed on the desk, he slid and landed onto her lap. The principal lectured and warned Billy that if the owl was to return, he would call the police.

9. Wol's favorite pastime was riding on people's shoulders. Billy's father's friend would wear a cap with ear-flaps (even in the summertime) so that Wol wouldn't nibble on his ears.

10. Wol liked to tease Mutt while Mutt was taking his afternoon nap. Mutt, of course, didn't enjoy Wol's fun activities.

11. The family and Bruce went in their caravan on a camping trip. Owls and crows don't get along. The crows tried to attack Wol, Billy's father had to take out his shotgun.

12. Billy's father took a new job in Toronto so the family had to move. Bruce who now lived on a fox farm took care of Wol and Weeps.

45

46

44